CLAUDE
Anyone for Strawberries?

BASED ON THE *Alex T Smith* CLAUDE STORIES
DEVISED FOR TELEVISION BY *Sixteen South*

Sir Bobblysock is not usually a big fan of early mornings, so Claude did not expect to find him already up and about at the crack of dawn one sunny day.

"Do you know what day it is, Claude?" said Sir Bobblysock.

"It's . . . ummm . . . Tuesday!" said Claude, yawning.

"Yes!" said Sir Bobblysock. "Strawberries-for-Breakfast day! My favourite day of the week!"

Of course it was!

"Strawberries, here we come!" said Claude, popping on his beret.

But Sir Bobblysock was already on his way!

Claude and Sir Bobblysock raced to find Denzel's fruit-and-veg van – but oh, dear! He was fresh out of strawberries!

"They've all been snapped up for the Pawhaven Tennis Championship in the park," he explained.

Sir Bobblysock dashed off just as fast as his bobbles could carry him.
"Come on, Claude!" he called. "To the park!"

No sooner had they reached the park,
than a tennis ball dropped out of the sky.
It was heading straight for Sir Bobblysock!

Quick as a flash, Claude jumped into the
air and caught the ball in his trusty beret.

"What a great catch!" said Sir Bobblysock. "You're ever so good."

"We'd better give the ball back," said Claude, thoughtfully.
"Come on, Sir Bobblysock!"

The semi-final was very much *not* in progress.
"I'm not playing without my lucky ball," huffed Errol Heart-Throb.

"I've got it!" said Claude, handing over the tennis ball.

"THANK YOU, CLAUDE," said Lord Turret, sitting on a very high chair that made him feel very important. "WE KEEP LOSING THE BALLS. I WISH WE HAD AN OFFICIAL BALL BOY TO BRING THEM BACK TO US."

Claude's ears wobbled and his tail waggled . . .

His eyebrows wiggled and he cried –

"I CAN DO THAT!"

"EXCELLENT!" said Lord Turret.

"And I can go and get some strawberries!" said Sir Bobblysock.

While Claude got on with the job, Sir Bobblysock took his place at the back of the queue for Mr Lovelybuns' strawberries.

But when he finally reached the front, there was bad news. *Very* bad news indeed . . .

"Sorry," said Mr Lovelybuns. "No more strawberries."

Sir Bobblysock summoned up all his socky strength to say one word. It was quite a long one:

"NOOOOOOO!!!"

Back on the tennis court, Claude ran this way and that after the ball.

Miss Highkick-Spin sent the tennis ball rocketing towards Errol, who squealed and jumped out of the way.

But the ball landed outside the line – so Miss Highkick-Spin lost the game!

"ERROL WINS AND GOES THROUGH TO THE GRAND FINAL!" declared Lord Turret.

"Are you OK, Errol?" asked Claude, helping him check his hair in his handy hand mirror.

"Argh!" shrieked the big movie star. "I can't play on looking like this. You'll have to take my place, Claude!"

Errol hurried away before anyone could notice that he had a few hairs out of place.

"Sir Bobblysock, guess what!" cried Claude. "I'm in the Pawhaven Tennis Championship final and you won't believe what the grand prize is . . .

A great big cup filled with strawberries!"

Sir Bobblysock gasped, like this:

"GASP!"

"I wonder who you're playing
against . . . ?" he said.

The answer was Kimberly, and she was jolly excited about it.

"Claude! I'm in the final too!" squeaked Kimberly. "I've never won anything before! In my whole life! Ever!"

"Is that racket regulation size?" wondered Sir Bobblysock. But, before there was any time for further enquiry, Lord Turret shouted –

"PLAY!"

And the game began!

First Kimberly was in the lead.

The crowd ooohed.

And then it was Claude.

The crowd aaahed.

And then the score was even.

"Oooh!"

"Aaah!"

"NEXT POINT WINS THE FINAL!" boomed Lord Turret.

The crowd was too tense to make any noise at all.

Kimberly and Claude hit the ball back and forth, until Kimberly hit it *very* hard. So hard that her tennis racket went flying too!

The ball bounced very high and very far.

Claude dashed after
it. He ran through
the playground . . .

He ran past the crazy golf course . . .

He ran all the way to the duck pond where the ball *didn't* hit the ground –
it bounced off a park bench . . .

BA-DOING!

and flew all the way back to . . .

. . . . the tennis court!

"I haven't got my racket," said Kimberly. "What am I going to do?"

Claude felt sad. "I can't beat Kimberly like this," he said.
"She hasn't got her racket. It's not fair."

He let the ball hit the ground.

DOINK!

"GAME, SET AND MATCH TO KIMBERLY!" yelled Lord Turret.

Kimberly was thrilled! Her first ever win! At anything! Ever!

"I hope you don't mind that I missed the last shot on purpose, Sir Bobblysock," whispered Claude.

"You did the right thing," said Sir Bobblysock. "Just look how happy Kimberly is with her win."

She *did* look very happy.

"But you didn't get your strawberries for breakfast," sighed Claude.

"There'll be other Tuesdays," said Sir Bobblysock.

"Ooooh – I'm allergic to strawberries," said Kimberly, scritch-scratching. "I'm getting a bit itchy just thinking about it! Would you like them?"

"Well, if you insist!"
said Sir Bobblysock.

Claude whipped out a bowl
from his beret.

Sir Bobblysock was delighted.

"THAT WAS THE MOST EXCITING CHAMPIONSHIP EVER!" yelled Lord Turret. "I SAY, CLAUDE – HOW WOULD YOU LIKE TO BECOME A FULL-TIME MEMBER OF THE PAWHAVEN TENNIS CLUB?"

"Ummm . . ." said Claude, having a think. "No, thank you, Lord Turret. It was lots of fun, but I don't think I'd enjoy chasing balls all the time. And Sir Bobblysock and I have some strawberries to eat!"

"We certainly do," said Sir Bobblysock, slapping his chops at the prospect.

Later on, Claude was curled up in his bed at 112 Waggy Avenue when Mr and Mrs Shinyshoes returned home.

"My goodness!" said Mrs Shinyshoes. "Where did that tennis racket come from? And look at that bowl of strawberries."

"You don't think Claude would know anything about it, do you?" asked Mr Shinyshoes.

"Of course not," said Mrs Shinyshoes. "Claude's been fast asleep all day."

But Claude *did* know something about it.
And we do too, don't we?

HODDER CHILDREN'S BOOKS

First Published in Great Britain in 2019
by Hodder and Stoughton

1 3 5 7 9 10 8 6 4 2

Based on the original 'Claude' series
published by Hodder Children's Books,
written and illustrated by Alex T. Smith

Storybook text written by Davey Moore

Copyright in images and script for
Anyone for Strawberries? written by Sean Carson
© 2019 Sixteen South Limited

A CIP catalogue record for this book
is available from the British Library.

ISBN 978 1 444 93862 3

Printed and bound in China

Hodder Children's Books
An imprint of Hachette Children's Group
Part of Hodder and Stoughton
Carmelite House
50 Victoria Embankment
London, EC4Y ODZ

An Hachette UK Company
www.hachette.co.uk
www.hachettechildrens.co.uk

FSC
www.fsc.org
MIX
Paper from
responsible sources
FSC® C104740

First published in 2012
by Hodder Children's Books
This paperback edition published in 2013.

Copyright © Mick Inkpen 2012

Hodder Children's Books
338 Euston Road, London NW1 3BH

Hodder Children's Books Australia
Level 17/207 Kent Street, Sydney, NSW 2000

The right of Mick Inkpen to be identified as the author
and illustrator of this Work has been asserted by him in
accordance with the Copyright, Designs and Patents Act 1988.

A catalogue record of this book is
available from the British Library.

ISBN: 978 1 444 90821 3
10 9 8 7 6 5 4 3 2 1

Printed in China

Hodder Children's Books is a
division of Hachette Children's Books,
an Hachette UK Company
www.hachette.co.uk

Wibbly Pig

picks a pet

Hodder
Children's
Books

A division of Hachette Children's Books

'Guess what!' says Wibbly Pig. 'Big Pig's sister's friend is getting a new pet today!'

It is true. Big Pig's sister's friend is off to the

et shop with her pocket money.

'What do you think she'll choose?' says Scruffy Pig. 'I bet it will be something boring. Something really boring, like a hamster. . .

or a goldfish. . .

or a rabbit!

Yes, that's what she'll choose, a **rabbit!**'

'Oh no, not a **rabbit!**'

'If you could choose,' says
Wibbly Pig. 'If you could choose
anything, anything at all,
what would YOU
choose?'

'Anything at all?'
says Scruffy Pig.

'Anything,
except a rabbit.'

'I'd choose an **elephant!** We could have a water fight with an elephant!

You can't do **that** with a rabbit!'

'I'd have a bear!
Bears are best.
Especially polar bears!
Much better than
a rabbit!'

'It would be
cool to have a
kangaroo!

Tiny Pig could
go for a ride
in the pouch!

You can't do that
with a rabbit!'

'We could have **giraffes!** We could see for miles on a giraffe!'

'You can't
do that
with a rabbit
either.'

'Or what about a dolphin!'

wheeeeeeeeeeeeeeeeeeee

'I bet she won't choose anything like **this!**' says Scruffy Pig.

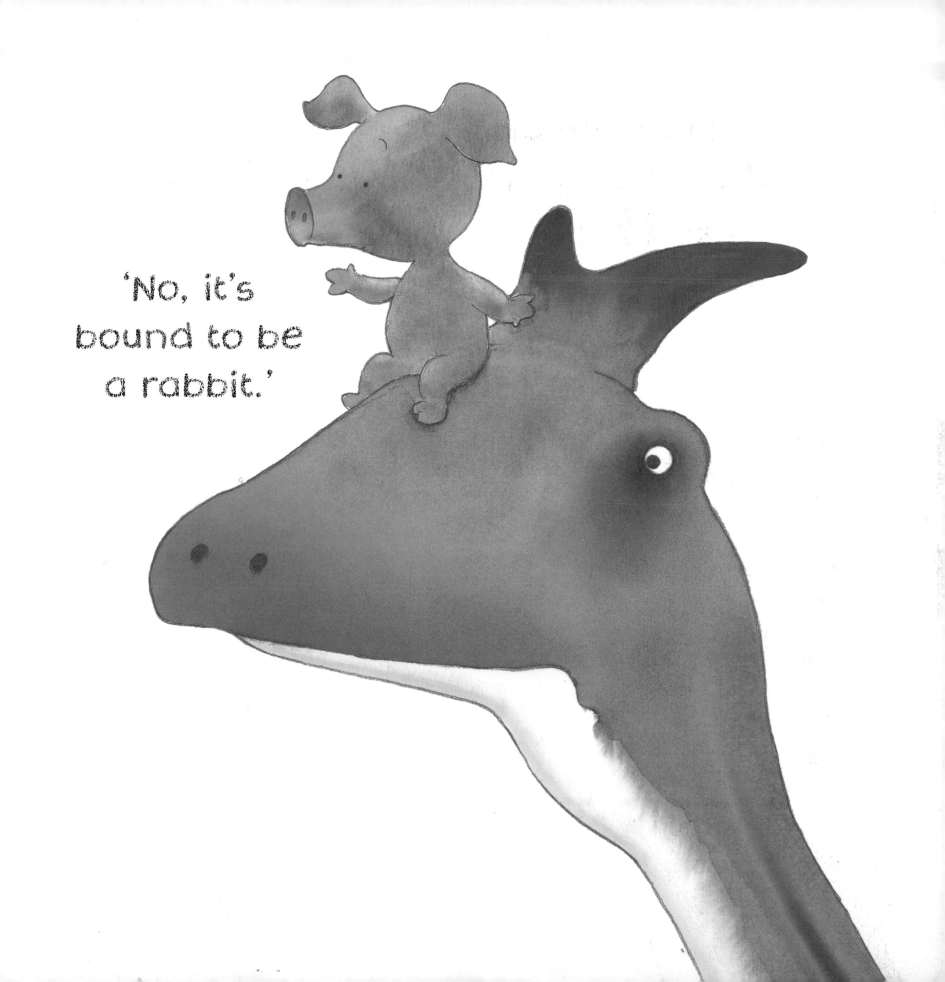

'No, it's
bound to be
a rabbit.'

And sure enough,
when Big Pig's sister's
friend comes back from
the pet shop she has a large,
brown and white. . .

. . . .rabbit.

'Thought so,'
says Wibbly Pig.

'Boring!' whispers
Scruffy Pig.

But,
the rabbit hops onto
Scruffy Pig's lap.
It licks his face.

(He forgets about the elephant.)

Then it licks Wibbly.

(He forgets about the polar bear and the kangaroo.)